THE WORKING ENTREPRENEUR NOTEBOOK

This Planner belongs to:

_____

_____

INTRODUCTION

I'm so excited to.....NEVERMIND

For you Because this book isn't about me, it's all about you, your goals and how you are about to crush them!! Congratulations on deciding to level-up your business mindset while punching the clock. The content and activities in this journal are intentionally created by me for YOU.

Should you become an entrepreneur or should you work a 9 to 5?

That's a question that only you can answer!

Use this notebook to help you decide what's best for you!

Can you handle both?

Is it good to work a 9 to 5?

Without a doubt, yes.

Can you do both? Yes, if you can!!

ENTREPRENEUR

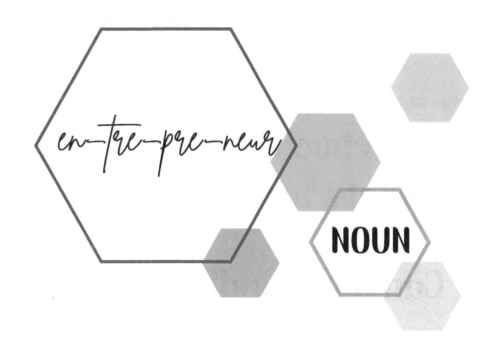

en-tre-pre-neur

NOUN

Entrepreneurship refers to the process of creating a new enterprise and bearing any of its risk with the view of making profit.

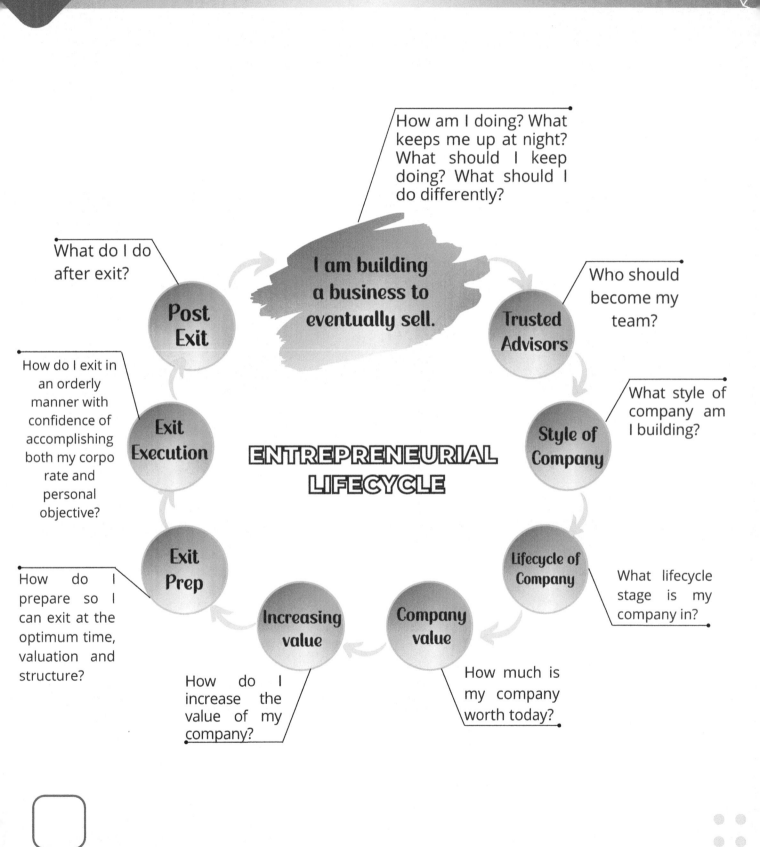

Many people operate a side business while working a full-time job.

This experience can be rewarding personally, professionally and financially.

However, this shit is not easy and it takes time.

WHAT IT TAKES TO BE AN ENTREPRENEUR

If you want to succeed as an entrepreneur, it's going to take thinking like an entrepreneur. You need to be the person you want to become, think like the person you want to become before you have success as that person. That's what it's going to take!

Use the next 3 pages for MILLIONNAIRE AFFIRMATIONS.

SEEN IT ON SOCIAL MEDIA. WRITE IT HERE.

....

....

....

....

....

....

....

....

....

....

....

QUOTES

....

....

....

....

....

....

....

....

....

....

....

....

....

....

....

....

QUOTES

QUOTES

Employees tend to avoid failure. Entrepreneurs will go after failure because they're pro-risk.

EMPLOYEE (9AM-5PM)	ENTREPRENEUR 24 HOURS
Work for others	Own boss
Security	Freedom
Income is fixed (Salary)	Income is risky
Sick days are covered	Don't work-Don't eat
Nobody has to know what you do	You are your brand at all times

Set Business hours and stick to them. Use this page to decide what hours work best for you.

WORK SCHEDULE

MONDAY	TUESDAY	WEDNESDAY	THURSDAY	FRIDAY	SATURDAY	SUNDAY

BUSINESS HOURS

MONDAY		TO	
TUESDAY		TO	
WEDNESDAY		TO	
THURSDAY		TO	
FRIDAY		TO	
SATURDAY		TO	
SUNDAY		TO	

If you are giving a job 40 hours a week you need to give your business 80 hours a week.

What's stopping you for quitting your 9 to 5?

FILL IN THE BLANKS

I want to have .... saved to cover my ass.

I need enough money to purchase ....

My credit score is ....

I will walk out the MF on ....

My boss is an ...., I will not be that kind of a boss.

NOTES

NOTES

What's keeping you at your 9 to 5?
-THAT'S FOR SHOW MONEY $$

Remember if I don't hustle - my kids don't eat!

NOTES

The focus is entrepreneurs is getting better at what they're already great at. List all the things you are great at.

....

....

....

....

....

....

....

....

....

....

....

....

....

....

....

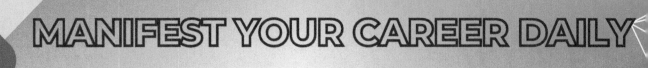

MANIFEST YOUR CAREER DAILY

DATE:	My mood today is:
I am manifesting	**My why is ....**
My word of the day or affirmation:	**Mind dump any negative thoughts:**
Visualize **I see, I feel, I own, I earn, I have........**	**Actions I will take today to get to my goals:**
I will accomplish these 2 tasks today:	**I am thankful for ....**

MANIFEST YOUR CAREER DAILY

DATE:

My mood today is:

I am manifesting ....

My why is ....

My word of the day or affirmation:

Mind dump any negative thoughts:

Visualize
I see, I feel, I own, I earn, I have........

Actions I will take today to get to my goals:

I will accomplish these 2 tasks today:

I am thankful for ....

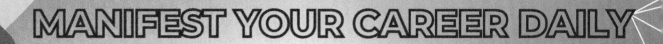

MANIFEST YOUR CAREER DAILY

DATE:

My mood today is:

I am manifesting ....

My why is ....

My word of the day or affirmation:

Mind dump any negative thoughts:

Visualize
I see, I feel, I own, I earn, I have........

Actions I will take today to get to my goals:

I will accomplish these 2 tasks today:

I am thankful for ....

MANIFEST YOUR CAREER DAILY

DATE:

My mood today is:

I am manifesting ....

My why is ....

My word of the day or affirmation:

Mind dump any negative thoughts:

Visualize
I see, I feel, I own, I earn, I have........

Actions I will take today to get to my goals:

I will accomplish these 2 tasks today:

I am thankful for ....

MANIFEST YOUR CAREER DAILY

DATE:

My mood today is:

I am manifesting ....

My why is ....

My word of the day or affirmation:

Mind dump any negative thoughts:

Visualize
I see, I feel, I own, I earn, I have........

Actions I will take today to get to my goals:

I will accomplish these 2 tasks today:

I am thankful for ....

MANIFEST YOUR CAREER DAILY

DATE:

My mood today is:

I am manifesting ....

My why is ....

My word of the day or affirmation:

Mind dump any negative thoughts:

Visualize
I see, I feel, I own, I earn, I have........

Actions I will take today to get to my goals:

I will accomplish these 2 tasks today:

I am thankful for ....

MANIFEST YOUR CAREER DAILY

DATE:

My mood today is:

I am manifesting ....

My why is ....

My word of the day or affirmation:

Mind dump any negative thoughts:

Visualize
I see, I feel, I own, I earn, I have........

Actions I will take today to get to my goals:

I will accomplish these 2 tasks today:

I am thankful for ....

Your passion deserves your attention.

DON'T HALF-ASS THIS SECTION

TAKE YOUR TIME AND THINK

QUESTIONS TO ASK YOURSELF

What are my motivations for owning a business?

QUESTIONS TO ASK YOURSELF

Should I start or buy a business?

QUESTIONS TO ASK YOURSELF

What and where is the market for what you want to sell?

....

....

....

....

....

....

....

....

....

....

....

....

....

....

QUESTIONS TO ASK YOURSELF

How much will all this cost me?

QUESTIONS TO ASK YOURSELF

Should my business have a store front, be online or both?

....

....

....

....

....

....

....

....

....

....

....

....

....

....

GOALS

GOALS

....

....

....

....

....

....

....

....

....

....

....

....

....

....

....

....

GOALS

GOALS

GOALS

ENTREPRENEURS ARE MADE, NOT BORN!

MONTHLY GOALS

JAN

GOAL

....

....

....

....

....

....

Plans to reach my Goal

....

....

....

....

....

....

....

MONTHLY GOALS FEB

GOAL

....

....

....

....

....

Plans to reach my Goal

....

....

....

....

....

....

....

GOAL

....

....

....

....

....

....

Plans to reach my Goal

....

....

....

....

....

....

....

....

MONTHLY GOALS

GOAL

....
....
....
....
....

Plans to reach my Goal

....
....
....
....
....
....
....

GOAL

....

....

....

....

....

....

Plans to reach my Goal

....

....

....

....

....

....

....

MONTHLY GOALS

JUN

GOAL

....

....

....

....

....

Plans to reach my Goal

....

....

....

....

....

....

GOAL

....

....

....

....

....

....

Plans to reach my Goal

....

....

....

....

....

....

....

....

....

MONTHLY GOALS

AUG

GOAL

....
....
....
....
....
....

Plans to reach my Goal

....
....
....
....
....
....
....
....
....

GOAL

....
....
....
....
....

Plans to reach my Goal

....
....
....
....
....
....
....

MONTHLY GOALS

GOAL

....
....
....
....
....
....
....

Plans to reach my Goal

....
....
....
....
....
....
....
....

GOAL

....

....

....

....

....

....

Plans to reach my Goal

....

....

....

....

....

....

....

....

GOAL

Plans to reach my Goal

Let's Talk Financing-Most of the money needed to start a new business comes from the entrepreneur.

Use the next two pages to write down how you will fund your business.
Don't fool yourself into thinking you have more than you do.

You can't grow if you can't be honest with your damn self.

Do it do it with passion or don't do it at all. Think you're ready? Can you crush this thing without a 9 to 5.

INCOME	VS	EXPENSES

Identify what's working. Remember some things. Take time.

Identify what's not working.

EXAMPLES: Set a schedule and stick to it. Say "no" to things that aren't on your priority list. Don't take on more client work when you're at your max. Don't overschedule yourself. Use this space to set boundries .... and stick to them!

Being a working entrepreneur is not all peaches and cream. You may not have "BOSS" but your personal life is still controlled by your customers.

Remember to rest

Juggling your 9-5 side hustle and all of your many other responsibilities can be hard. No matter how much you love what you're doing, burnout is very much real and it's so easy to become lazy and unmotivated.

Recognizing the signs of Burnout

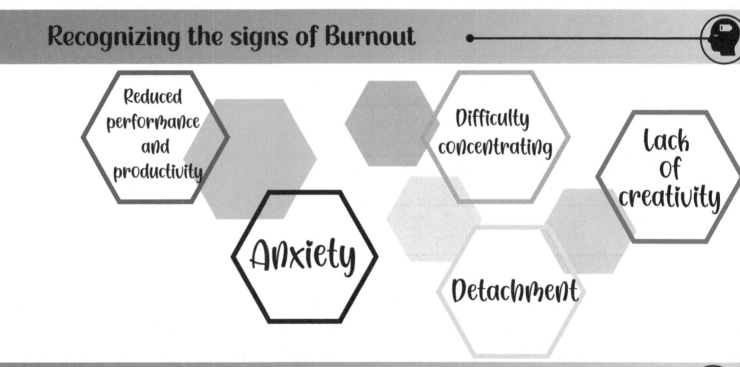

Reduced performance and productivity

Anxiety

Difficulty concentrating

Detachment

Lack of creativity

Find Balance in your Life

TAKE A VACATION - It will help you be so much more productive, efficient and happy!

Use up your sick/vacation days so that you are still getting a CHECK!! $$$$

Use this page to plan your next trip!

VACATION

Do what makes you happy!

Celebrate your WINS!!!

Take each day one step at a time. Everyday is not perfect, but you can always find happiness in the little things. Drive deep into your thoughts and feelings with monthly reflections as you practice balance. Use these pages for monthly reflections,

....

....

....

....

....

....

....

....

....

....

....

....

....

MONTHLY REFLECTIONS

JANUARY

RATE THE MONTH ON SCALE OF 1-10

BEST MOMENT OF THIS MONTH

Things I Achieved

CHALLENGES EXPERIENCED	HOW I OVERCOME THEM

MONTHLY REFLECTIONS

FEBURARY

RATE THE MONTH ON SCALE OF 1-10

BEST MOMENT OF THIS MONTH

Things I Achieved

....

....

....

....

....

....

CHALLENGES EXPERIENCED	HOW I OVERCOME THEM

MONTHLY REFLECTIONS

MARCH

RATE THE MONTH ON SCALE OF 1-1[0]

BEST MOMENT OF THIS MONTH

Things I Achieved

CHALLENGES EXPERIENCED	HOW I OVERCOME THEM

MONTHLY REFLECTIONS

APRIL

RATE THE MONTH ON SCALE OF 1-10

BEST MOMENT OF THIS MONTH

Things I Achieved

CHALLENGES EXPERIENCED	HOW I OVERCOME THEM

MONTHLY REFLECTIONS

MAY

BEST MOMENT OF THIS MONTH

Things I Achieved

CHALLENGES EXPERIENCED

HOW I OVERCOME THEM

MONTHLY REFLECTIONS

JUNE

RATE THE MONTH ON SCALE OF 1-10

BEST MOMENT OF THIS MONTH

Things I Achieved

CHALLENGES EXPERIENCED

HOW I OVERCOME THEM

MONTHLY REFLECTIONS

JULY

BEST MOMENT OF THIS MONTH

Things I Achieved

CHALLENGES EXPERIENCED	HOW I OVERCOME THEM

MONTHLY REFLECTIONS

AUGUST

BEST MOMENT OF THIS MONTH

Things I Achieved

....

....

....

....

....

....

....

CHALLENGES EXPERIENCED	HOW I OVERCOME THEM

MONTHLY REFLECTIONS

SEPTEMBER

RATE THE MONTH ON SCALE OF 1-10

BEST MOMENT OF THIS MONTH

Things I Achieved

CHALLENGES EXPERIENCED	HOW I OVERCOME THEM

MONTHLY REFLECTIONS

OCTOBER

RATE THE MONTH ON SCALE OF 1-10

BEST MOMENT OF THIS MONTH

Things I Achieved

CHALLENGES EXPERIENCED

HOW I OVERCOME THEM

MONTHLY REFLECTIONS

NOVEMBER

RATE THE MONTH ON SCALE OF 1-1

BEST MOMENT OF THIS MONTH

Things I Achieved

CHALLENGES EXPERIENCED	HOW I OVERCOME THEM

MONTHLY REFLECTIONS

DECEMBER

RATE THE MONTH ON SCALE OF 1-10

BEST MOMENT OF THIS MONTH

Things I Achieved

CHALLENGES EXPERIENCED	HOW I OVERCOME THEM

DOCTOR VISIT

See your doctor: Your health is important and helps with balancing working a 9 to 5 and being a bomb ass entrepreneur.

DATES	TIME

Write a note to your future self!

....

....

....

....

....

....

....

....

....

....

....

....

....

....

....

You're about to live and breathe your dream.

DO IT WITH PASSION, PROPER PLANNING AND EXECUTION, YOUR BEST DAYS ARE AHEAD OF YOU!!